Soccer is the most popular sport
In the sunny small town of Oakcrest.
All the boys and girls play together on weekends.
Patrick Ford is considered one of the best.

Patrick's team is the Purple Thunderbolts.
With the Red Dragons, they have a long-standing feud.
We join them after their match on a crisp autumn Saturday
When Patrick is in a rather grumpy mood.

Patrick mumbles his "good games."
The high-fives he gives his opponents are weak.
His head is down while he slinks to his dad's car,
And as he gets in, he barely wants to speak.

"I played poorly almost the entire first half.
I was distracted and not using my brain.
Plus I should have scored another goal,"
Patrick says to his dad, trying to explain.

Mr. Ford is pleased his son has high standards.
There's always room for improvement!
"We can run some drills together when we
get home," he offers,
"To work on your field positioning and movement."

"I'd like to train footwork with you," Patrick says,
"But that's not why I'm mad or what's wrong."

"Are you frustrated with a teammate then?" Dad asks.
"Because not everyone has your work ethic or is as strong?"

"Keeping giving best efforts at practice and games
And figure out which skills you need to enhance.

Be a patient leader with the weaker kids now
And by tryouts next season you should be ready to advance."

"I'm not angry about that," Patrick scowls.
"It's how the other team played, especially Nicole.
She fouled me in the first half, a total cheap shot!
Just as I was about to score the Thunderbolts' first goal."

"It was a dirty play," Mr. Ford agrees,
"That's why the ref gave her a yellow card and a penalty.
Her coach was furious and called her to the sidelines
And for the next ten minutes, she had to take a knee."

"But it's not fair," Patrick says. "If a boy had shoved me like Nicole did,
I would have shoved him back twice as hard."

"Then your whole team would have suffered,"
Patrick's dad retorts,
"Because you'd have been benched with a red card."

"It's not fair," Patrick repeats. "Because Nicole's a girl,
I'm supposed to treat her differently and can't
play at my prime."

"Is that really true?" Dad pushes back. "From where I
was standing,
It looked like you were battling her for the ball every time."

Mr. Ford sighs as he breaks at a stoplight.
He's a grownup, but sometimes he feels confused too.
"Nicole started it today, unprovoked" Patrick continues,
"So what's a boy like me supposed to do?"

"When it comes to interacting with girls," his dad begins,
"There isn't a rulebook. It's a matter of judgment,
not fact.

But our family has certain principles that can guide you
As to how a young gentleman should act."

"In a soccer match, there are coaches and refs
To ensure the game is played fairly and you're all
treated the same.
Each player has different strengths and weaknesses
And you've agreed to put them to the test in the game."

"So from my perspective," Mr. Ford continues,
"In sports it's okay to be aggressive, just not
unnecessarily rough.
It's part of the game for a girl like Nicole,
Who's an athlete, a competitor, she's tough!"

Patrick thinks about this carefully.
"So if we're truly equals, why can't I be a cheap shot back?

When Nicole's the one who started it,
And there's no strength or skill that girls lack?"

"Plus you've always told me I shouldn't start a fight
But I sure as heck can finish it.

Then again, at school expulsion is the punishment for
any fight at all,
And even claiming self-defense won't diminish it."

Mr. Ford is filled with compassion
As he glances back at Patrick in the rearview mirror.
Being a virtuous boy seemed simpler when he was a kid.
Nowadays, even what constitutes good manners
can be unclear.

"We know Nicole and her family well,"
Mr. Ford says, carefully choosing each word.
"And if you let her win just because she's a girl
She'll be offended and think it's absurd."

"Nicole and the other girls know how the sport is played.
They know it's not the time for flowers and frills.

So you shouldn't hesitate to steal the ball or be aggressive —
It's a sign of respect for their athletic skills."

Mr. Ford chuckles loudly at his son's remark.
"I wish I could tell you it's easy, son, but it ain't.

You should be strong and courageous and fight if you must,
Yet it's almost always it's best to show self-restraint."

"If you're protecting yourself or your siblings
You won't get in trouble with your mom or with me.

But you must try to diffuse the situation
before it escalates to that,
With the other boys too, but with the girls especially."

"I just want to be sure," Patrick begins.
"It doesn't matter that Nicole and I are the same height?

And we both did six chin-ups in gym class last week,
So we'd be equally matched if she really wants to fight!"

Mr. Ford laughs as he pulls into their driveway.
"Yes, even though you're equally strong right now.

Son, it's not easy learning to become an honorable man.
But I'm here to help you figure out how."

"Other families might have different principles than ours,"
Mr. Ford concludes as he parks the car.

"Strength, perseverance, temperance, and sportsmanship
Are some of the values that make us Ford men who we are."

Now that they're home, Patrick drops his bag in the kitchen,
He hugs his mom and checks how long until dinner will begin.

Mr. Ford is as proud of his boy for his insightful questions
As he is for the Thunderbolts' win.

There's still enough time before dinner
For Patrick and his dad to run drills in the backyard.

The conversation on the way home was a different
kind of challenge,
But Patrick doesn't back down just because something is hard.

At recess on Monday, Nicole finds Patrick on the playground. She'd gotten caught up in the heat of the game, by her own admission.

Patrick values Nicole's friendship and has already moved past it,

And Nicole is his first pick for the day's kickball competition.

Have a bright & happy day!

Ingram Content Group UK Ltd.
Milton Keynes UK
UKHW052017090323
418352UK00009B/40